PRENTICE HALL MATHEMATICS

ALGEBRA 1
ALGEBRA 2

Hands-On Activities

Prentice
Hall

Needham, Massachusetts
Upper Saddle River, New Jersey
Glenview, Illinois

Copyright © 2004 by Pearson Education, Inc., publishing as Prentice Hall, Upper Saddle River, New Jersey 07458. All rights reserved. Printed in the United States of America. This publication is protected by copyright, and permission should be obtained from the publisher prior to any prohibited reproduction, storage in a retrieval system, or transmission in any form or by any means, electronic, mechanical, photocopying, recording, or likewise. The publisher hereby grants permission to reproduce these pages, in part or in whole, for classroom use only, the number not to exceed the number of students in each class. Notice of copyright must appear on all copies. For information regarding permission(s), write to: Rights and Permissions Department.

ISBN: 0-13-063385-2

2 3 4 5 6 7 8 9 10   06 05 04 03 02

Hands-On Activities

Contents

Contents (continued)

To the Teacher

The pages contained within this supplement are designed to engage students in tactile activities that promote the understanding of topics taught in the Prentice Hall *Algebra 1* and *Algebra 2* textbooks.

All students can benefit from participating in these activities, especially tactile learners. The activities are designed for students to physically engage in activities that lead to better comprehension of a topic. Many of the activities guide students to explore more advanced meanings of a topic.

Some activities are best suited as an introduction to a topic. For example, Activity 2 can serve nicely to introduce the topic of subtracting integers. Students use algebra tiles or two-color counters to model a subtraction equation.

Other activities are more suitable as extensions of textbook learning. For example, Activity 19 allows students to further explore Lesson 8-8 topics including independent versus dependent variables and related versus inversely related quantities. Students then graph the results of the activity.

Due to the nature of these activities, students who participate and explore the topics covered on the pages of this supplement are more likely to remember the topics taught. Tactile learners will have the experience of hands-on learning, while all learners will have memories from which to draw when recalling particular content for assessment.

These activities provide students with multiple ways to learn algebra. Have fun with your students.

Activity 1: Zero Out

• •

MATERIALS: Number cubes

This game can be played with 2 or more players.

You will need one number cube and paper and pencil for each player.

1   odd

−1

Rules:

1. The first player rolls the number cube twice. The first roll gives the first number and the second roll determines the sign of that number. An odd number means a negative sign and an even number means a positive sign. Players record their numbers.

2. The players take turns rolling the number cube twice until each player has 3 signed numbers.

3. Each player then uses their signed numbers to try and make sums that zero out.

4. The player who can do so with their first 3 numbers wins. If not, play continues one double roll at a time until one player can zero out.

Player 1

1   odd   2   even   2   odd

−1   +2   −2

−1 + 2 + (−2) = −1

3   odd

−3

−1 + (−3) = −4

no

Player 2

3   even   6   odd   4   even

+3   −6   +4

3 + (−6) + 4 = 1

1   odd

−1

1 + (−1) = 0   **Zero Out**

• •

Activity 2: Subtracting Integers

MATERIALS: Algebra tiles or two-color counters

To subtract integers using tiles:

| Use negative tiles or positive tiles to show the first integer. | → | If necessary, add pairs of positive and negative tiles. | → | Take away the appropriate tiles. | → | Count the remaining tiles. |

Subtract: $-6 - (-2)$

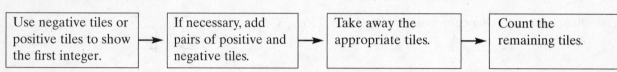

$-6 - (-2) = -4$

Subtract: $2 - (-5)$

2 can also be modeled by
adding the same number
of positive and negative tiles.

$2 - (-5) = 7$

Write a subtraction equation for each model.

1. ☐☐☐ → ☐☐☐☐☐ → ☐☐☐☐☐ → ☐☐☐☐☐
        ☐☐   ☒☒

2. ☐ → ☐☐☐☐ → ☒☒☒☒ → ☐☐☐
    ☐☐☐   ☐☐☐

Subtract. Use tiles if necessary.

3. $-6 - 9 =$ _____   **4.** $6 - 9 =$ _____   **5.** $-5 - 7 =$ _____

6. $5 - 8 =$ _____   **7.** $-4 - 6 =$ _____   **8.** $4 - 6 =$ _____

9. $-3 - 9 =$ _____   **10.** $3 - 9 =$ _____   **11.** $-9 - 3 =$ _____

12. $9 - (-3) =$ _____   **13.** $-3 - (-9) =$ _____   **14.** $-9 - (-3) =$ _____

15. $-4 - 8 =$ _____   **16.** $4 - (-8) =$ _____   **17.** $-9 - 2 =$ _____

Activity 3: The Distributive Property

MATERIALS: Algebra tiles or two-color counters

You can illustrate the *Distributive Property of multiplication over addition* using tiles. This property tells you, for example, that $3(2 + 5)$ is the same as $3(2) + 3(5)$.

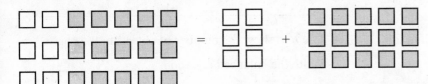

The 3 rows each containing 7 tiles are a model for the expression $3(2 + 5)$. We can rearrange these tiles to form two rectangles containing 6 and 15 tiles, respectively, to model the expression $3(2) + 3(5)$.

1. The procedure described shows that _____ = _____.

2. Model the expression $2(5 + 4)$. How many rows do you have? _____
   How many tiles are in each row? _____

3. Model the expression $2(5) + 2(4)$. You should have two rectangles. One
   rectangle contains _____ tiles, and the other contains _____ tiles.

Rewrite each expression using the Distributive Property.

4. $3(4 + y)$ _____

5. $2(n + 3)$ _____

6. $7(2x + 3)$ _____

7. $3(x + y)$ _____

8. $4(2c + d)$ _____

9. $5(p + 9q)$ _____

10. Is $3 \cdot 5 + 4$ the same as $3(5 + 4)$? _____

11. The Distributive Property can also be used in reverse. For example,
    start with two rectangles, one with 4 rows of 3 tiles each, and another
    with 4 rows of 2 tiles each. Rearrange these to form 4 rows of 5 tiles
    each. This shows that $4(3) + 4(2) =$ _____.

Rewrite each expression using the Distributive Property.

12. $5r + 5s$ _____

13. $3a + 6b$ _____

14. $2m + 2(3)$ _____

Using the Distributive Property to rewrite $3x + 15y$ as $3(x + 5y)$ is called taking out the *common factor* 3. The second expression is said to be in *factored* form.

Factor each expression.

15. $14a + 7b$ _____

16. $11u + 44$ _____

17. $3x + 3y + 3z$ _____

18. $35v + 7$ _____

19. $15x + 50y$ _____

20. $4a + 8b + 4c$ _____

Activity 4: Balancing Act

••

> **MATERIALS:** balance scale, paper bags, many small objects of equal weight

1. Practice balancing the scale.

   Place 5 objects inside a paper bag in the left pan.
   Place 5 objects in the right pan.

   Does the scale balance? _____

   Why? _____

   _____

2. This picture shows the balanced equation.

   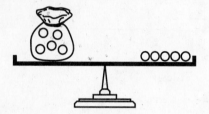

   Use *n* to show the number of objects in the bag.

   Write the balanced equation. _____

3. Add 4 objects to each side.

   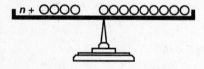

   Does the scale balance? _____

   Write the equation. _____

4. Take away 2 objects from each side.

   Does the scale balance? _____

   Write the equation. _____

5. Suppose someone saw the balance for the first time as it is now. Tell how they could decide how many objects are in the bag without looking inside.

   _____

   _____

   _____

6. Suppose you want to set up the balance scale to show $n + 13 = 21$. You can use a paper bag with objects inside to show the variable.

   How can you decide how many objects in the bag will balance the equation? _____

   _____

   _____

7. Can you find the answer by removing objects only from the left pan?

   Tell why or why not. _____

   _____

8. Use what you have learned to solve the equation for *n*. Remember that the equal sign means that the terms of the equation balance.

   $n + 13 = 21$

   $n + 13$ _____ $= 21$ _____

   $n =$ _____

Activity 5: Modeling Equations

MATERIALS: Algebra tiles

Solve the equation modeled in each equation box using algebra tiles. Shaded tiles are negative. Follow these rules for working with tiles.

Rules

A. You can add or remove tiles, but whatever you add to or remove from one side of the equation box you must *also* add to or remove from the *other side*.

B. Any pair of additive inverse tiles *on the same side* of an equation box add to zero and can be removed.

C. You can use one or more horizontal dotted lines to divide the equation box into identical equation boxes. Then continue to work with only one of these new boxes.

$2x = 4$ $x = 2$

Write the equation modeled in each equation box. Use the rules to get a single *x*-tile on one side of the equation box and only unit tiles on the other side. The number represented by the unit tiles is the value of *x*.

1.

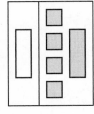

_____

2.

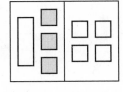

_____

3.

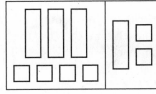

_____

4. Write your own equation. Then use algebra tiles to model the equation and solve for *x*.

_____

5. Write a paragraph describing how you applied the rules and any difficulties you had.

_____

_____

_____

Activity 6: Time to React

MATERIALS: meter stick

Work with a partner on this experiment.

Put your arm flat against the surface of a table or level desk. Your hand should extend just over the edge of the surface.

Have your partner hold a meter stick just above your hand. Your partner will drop the meter stick without giving you prior warning. As soon as you see it begin to drop, grab it as fast as you can.

Find the distance in centimeters that the meter stick dropped before you were able to grab it. This should be the measure on the meter stick just *above* your hand.

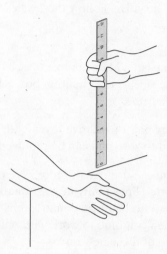

Now use the formula below to convert this distance into your reaction time. Substitute for *d* the distance the meter stick traveled, then solve for *t* (the time traveled, which is your reaction time).

FORMULA:

$$t = 4d + 90$$

d is the distance in centimeters.
t is your reaction time in milliseconds
(a millisecond is 1/1000 second).

1. Do the experiment six times. Record the distance the meter stick traveled each time, then use the formula above to calculate your reaction times.

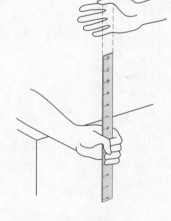

Trial 1: $d = $ _____   Trial 2: $d = $ _____

$t = $ _____ $t = $ _____

Trial 3: $d = $ _____   Trial 4: $d = $ _____

$t = $ _____ $t = $ _____

Trial 5: $d = $ _____   Trial 6: $d = $ _____

$t = $ _____ $t = $ _____

2. What is your average reaction time? _____

3. Did your reaction time improve over the trials? _____

4. What is the difference between your fastest and
slowest reaction times? _____

Activity 7: Too Big and Too Little

You are supposed to take your 8-year-old cousin Karen to the amusement park. She has been complaining that the kiddie rides are too babyish and that she cannot go on most of the big rides. Karen is 4 ft 5 in. tall.

Make graphs on the number lines of the age and height restrictions for the big rides. Label each graph with the name of the ride. Draw horizontal arrows for rides that require only height or age restrictions on the appropriate graph. For rides with both age and height restriction, draw a line connecting the two points.

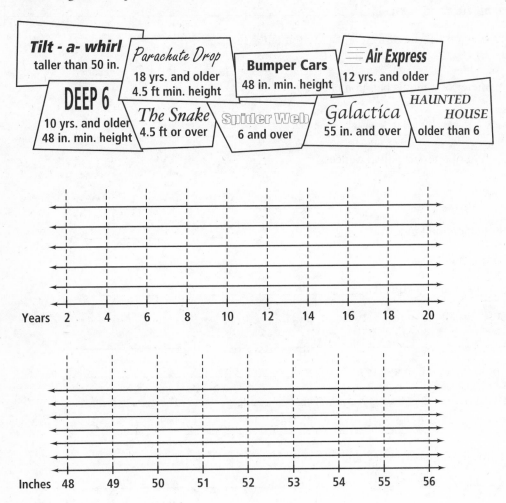

Put Karen on each number line to represent her age and height. Compare. Is Karen correct in her complaint about the big rides? Explain.

_____

_____

_____

Activity 8: Compound Inequalities

For most sports, there are not only rules of play, but rules that govern equipment that can be used in official play. For example, the diameter of a tennis ball must be greater than $2\frac{1}{2}$ in. but less than $2\frac{5}{8}$ in. The weight of the tennis ball must be greater than 2 oz but less than $2\frac{1}{16}$ oz.

The diameter and the weight requirements for a tennis ball can each be represented by a compound inequality. Recall that compound inequalities are two inequalities joined by the word *and* or the word *or*.

Work with a partner to complete Exercises 1–11.

Determine whether each statement is true or false. If the statement is false, rewrite it so that it is true.

1. If d represents the diameter of a tennis ball in inches, then $d > 2\frac{1}{2}$ and $d < 2\frac{5}{8}$.

    _____

2. If w represents the weight of a tennis ball in ounces, then $w > 2$ or $w < 2\frac{1}{16}$.

    _____

3. $d > 2\frac{1}{2}$ and $d < 2\frac{5}{8}$ is a compound inequality. _____

4. $w > 2$ or $w < 2\frac{1}{16}$ is equivalent to $2 < w < 2\frac{1}{16}$. _____

5. $w > 2$ or $w < 2\frac{1}{16}$ is a compound inequality. _____

6. $d > 2\frac{1}{2}$ or $d < 2\frac{5}{8}$ represent all diameters between $2\frac{1}{2}$ and $2\frac{5}{8}$.

    _____

7. $2 < w$ and $w < 2\frac{1}{16}$ is a compound inequality. _____

8. $2 > w < 2\frac{1}{16}$ _____

9. $2 < d < 2\frac{1}{16}$ _____

10. An official tennis ball must weigh between 2 and $2\frac{1}{16}$ oz.

    _____

11. The diameter of a golf ball must be at least 1.68 in. Find out more information about the size restrictions for golf balls. Then write five compound inequalities involving the measures of a golf ball.

    _____

    _____

    _____

Activity 9: Working With Ratios

MATERIALS: calculator; 8 pennies and 4 nickels (several sets are desirable); ruler; wooden pencil (six-sided)

Place a pencil (six-sided, wooden) on a table and balance a ruler across it, as shown. Put 8 pennies on one end and 4 nickels on the other end about equidistant from the middle of the ruler or pivot point. Move either stack of coins slightly until a balance is achieved.

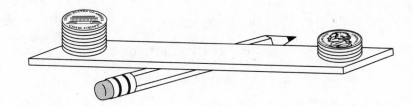

1. What is the ratio of the number of pennies to the number of nickels? This ratio is the constant of variation.

    _____

2. Remove two pennies and one nickel (very carefully) without changing the positions of the stacks of coins. What is the constant of variation now?

    _____

3. Let the number of pennies be given the symbol P and the number of nickels the symbol N. The ratio of P to N is the constant of variation. This result can be written as an equation of variation, as

    $$\frac{P}{N} = C$$

    where C is the constant of variation. If you had 100 nickels, solve this equation for the number of pennies required to balance the ruler.

    _____

4. You can write the pattern of pennies and nickels for balance as a set of ordered pairs of numbers; i.e., (2, 1), (4, 2), (8, 4) . . . Write the ordered pair for 100 nickels.

    _____

Activity 10: Examination Simulation

•••

MATERIALS: number cube

Work in a small group.

1. Suppose you do not know the answer to the multiple-choice question at the right. You guess. What is the probability of guessing the correct answer? _____

---

1. sjhgff erq rtzzzs mhy?

   A. always

   B. sometimes

   C. never

On a test there are ten multiple-choice questions like the one at the right. You guess at all the answers. You need at least five correct answers to pass the test.

2. Predict about how many answers you will answer correctly on the test.

3. What do you think your probability is for passing the test? Make a guess!

One way to find a probability that should be "in the ballpark" is to run an experiment, or **simulation.**

- Number a piece of paper from one through ten. Pretend you are taking the test by writing one of the letters (answers) **A, B, C,** after each number as if you were guessing the answer. Each person in your group should take the test.

- Make an answer key for your group as follows. Assign numbers from a number cube to the possible answer letters. (For example, the numbers one and two on the cube could stand for **A;** the numbers three and four could stand for **B;** and the numbers five and six could stand for **C.** In this way, each letter would have a $\frac{1}{3}$ chance of occurring. The number that is rolled tells you the correct answer for that question.

- Grade your test papers using this answer key.

An experimental probability for passing the test is given by the following ratio:

$$\frac{\text{number of students who passed the test}}{\text{total number of students who took the test}}$$

4. For your group, what was the experimental probability for passing the test?

5. Combine the results from your group with the results from other groups in the class. What was the experimental probability for passing the test for your class?

Group Discussion Questions

6. How did the individual group results compare with the combined results for the class?

7. Why do you think people run simulations?

Activity 11: Direct Measurement

• •

> **MATERIALS:** a clear jar or bottle, 2-ounce measuring cup, water, ruler, and graph paper

1. Before collecting any data, guess whether the *volume* of water and the *height* of water in a jar are directly related or inversely related quantities.

   _____

2. Pour 2 oz of water into an empty jar and measure the height. Record the data for volume and height in the table below. Add 2 oz more, measure the height, and record the new data. Repeat until you have data for at least three different volumes of water.

Volume (oz)	Height (cm)
2	

3. Graph the data on a coordinate plane with axes for volume and height. Does your scatter plot of the data show a *positive correlation*, a *negative correlation*, or *no correlation*?

   _____

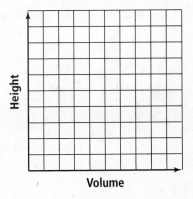

4. Recall that a line approximating a scatter plot is called a *trend line*. Draw a trend line for your scatter plot, and use your graph to describe the relationship between volume and height. Was your guess in Step 1 correct?

   _____

5. How could you use your graph to estimate what the height would be for a volume of 3 oz?

   _____

   _____

• •

Activity 12: Patterns in Folding

• •

MATERIALS: paper

---

1. Fold a sheet of paper in half. How many regions are formed in the paper? _____

2. How many regions are formed when you fold the paper in half twice? _____

   three times? _____

   What pattern do you notice between the number of folds and the number of regions? **Problem-Solving Tip:** Make an organized list and look for a pattern.

   _____

   _____

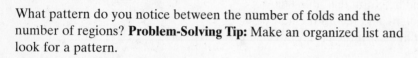

3. Write an expression for the number of regions formed when the paper is folded in half *n* times.

   _____

   Use it to predict the number of regions formed after 10 folds; 100 folds.

   _____

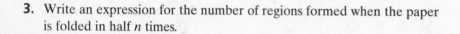

4. Write an expression for the portion of the whole sheet represented by one region after *n* folds.

   _____

   Use it to predict the portion of the whole sheet represented by one region after 10 folds; 100 folds.

   _____

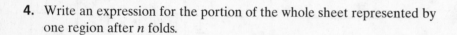

5. How are the expressions you wrote in Exercises 3 and 4 related? Describe how each quantity increases or decreases as the number of folds increases.

   _____

   _____

   _____

Activity 13: Sloping Binders

·· •

> **MATERIALS:** three-ring binder, ruler

Work with a group. Place a three-ring binder flat
on your desk. Notice how it slants downward
as you move from left to right.

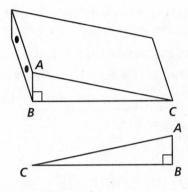

1. Measure the vertical distance from *A* to *B*.
   Record the distance in the space provided below.

   _____

2. Measure and record the horizontal distance from *B* to *C*.

   _____

3. Calculate the length from *A* to *B* divided by the length from *B* to *C*.
   Show your calculation below.

   _____

   _____

   _____

   This quotient approximates the slant, or *slope*, of the line from *A* to *C*.

4. Find the slope of the binders of all the people in your group.

   _____

   _____

5. Order the slopes from least to greatest.

   _____

   _____

Activity 14: Hidden Equation

Play this game against one opponent.

Write a simple equation such as $y = x + 6$ or $y = 2x + 3$ without letting your opponent see it.

Take turns guessing points on the grid. For each point named, the opponent must answer either "hit" or "miss."

- Hit indicates that the point named is on the graph of the equation.
- Miss indicates that the point named is not on the graph of the equation.

Continue guessing points until you think you can identify your opponent's equation. The first person who correctly identifies his or her opponent's equation wins.

1. How many points do you need to guess correctly to identify your opponent's hidden equation?

2. Which form of the equation will you use to figure out the equation?

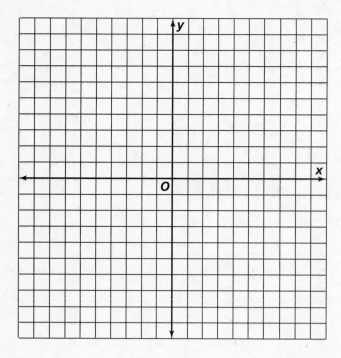

Activity 15: Pages and Weight

· ·

> **MATERIALS:** books for weighing, scale, graphing calculator

Work with a partner to complete Exercises 1–5.

1. Develop a hypothesis.
   - Give a qualitative description of the relationship between the weight of a book and the number of pages in the book.
   - Predict the form of the equation that models this relationship.

2. Run an experiment.
   - Find the number of pages in one of your textbooks and weigh the book.
   - Record the results in a table.
   - Find the total number of pages in two books and weigh the two books.
   - Record the results in the table.
   - Continue until you have the number of pages and weight of five books.

3. Represent data with graphs and equations.
   - Create a scatter plot.
   - Fit a trend line.
   - Calculate the equation for the line of best fit.

4. Compare the hypothesis and experimental result.
   - Did you and your partner predict the correct form of the equation?
   - If not, explain your choice of the equation in your hypothesis.

5. Make a prediction.
   - Pick a different book from the ones you used in the experiment. Note the number of pages and use your equation to find its weight.
   - Weigh the book.
   - How close are the actual and predicted weights?
   - If the weights are different, state two reasons that would explain the difference in the actual and predicted weights of the book.

Activity 16: What's the Point?

•••

MATERIALS: graph paper

Play the game "What's the Point?" in pairs.

Object of the Game: To locate your opponent's secret point on the coordinate plane by asking as few questions as possible.

* Choose a point on the coordinate plane. Write down coordinates of the point where your partner cannot see them. Each coordinate must be an integer from −10 to 10.

* To locate your partner's secret point, you will ask questions about either the *x*- or *y*- coordinate using the words *less than* or *greater than*. Your partner will answer using only *yes* or *no*. Keep a record of the number of questions you asked to locate your partner's secret point. Use a coordinate plane to delete all points each guess eliminates. When you think you have located your partner's secret point, you can guess what the coordinates of the point are. If your guess is incorrect, add three more questions to your total and continue to ask questions until you are ready to guess again.

* Switch roles with your partner to complete one round of the game. Whoever identifies the secret point with fewer questions wins the round. The first to win 3 rounds wins the game.

1. What was the fewest number of questions you needed to locate the secret point?

_____

2. If you were as lucky as possible, how many questions would you need to ask to locate the secret point? Explain with an example.

_____

_____

3. Suppose you choose a secret point on the coordinate plane, where each coordinate must be an integer from −*n* to *n*, where *n* is a very large number. How would you answer Exercise 2?

_____

4. How do inequalities help you locate the secret point?

_____

5. Describe a strategy for winning the game.

_____

_____

Activity 17: Where's the Intersection?
•••

MATERIALS: Graph paper and straightedge.

Work with a partner to complete Exercises 1–5.

Explore what happens when you graph two lines or linear inequalities on the same coordinate plane.

1. Can two lines be drawn with the given intersection? Support each answer with a diagram, an example, a real-life situation, or an explanation.

   a. a point

   b. a line

   c. a region

   d. no intersection

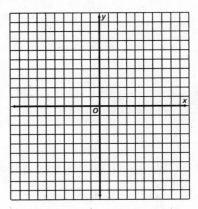

2. Can the graphs of two linear inequalities be drawn with the given intersection? Support your answer with a diagram, an example, a real-life situation, or an explanation.

   a. a point

   b. a line

   c. a region

   d. no intersection

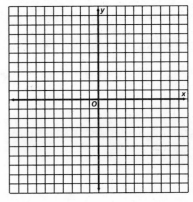

Summarize your findings for Exercises 1 and 2.

3. Compare the possible intersections of two lines with possible intersections of the graphs of two linear inequalities. What do you notice?

4. Find the possible intersections of more than two lines. Support each possibility with a diagram or an explanation.

5. Find the possible intersections for the graphs of more than two linear inequalities. Support each possibility with a diagram or an explanation.

Activity 18: Geometric Sequences

MATERIALS: thick construction paper, calipers, calculator

1. Measure the thickness of a flat sheet of construction paper. Be as accurate as you can.

2. Fold the paper in half and measure its thickness.

3. Fold it in half again and measure it.

4. Repeat this as many times as you can making sure the folded paper is flat when you measure it.

5. The measurements you've listed should be (approximately) a geometric sequence. List the ratio between each term: _____

6. Is there a common ratio? _____

7. Round the ratios to an integer. Now is there a common ratio? _____

8. If you could fold this paper 100 times, how thick would it be? _____

Use the diagram below to complete Exercises 9–12.

9. Write the sequence for the pattern.

   _____

10. Is the sequence geometric? Explain why or why not.

    _____

11. Find the 7th term of the sequence. _____

12. Write a formula for the sequence.

    _____

Activity 19: Bouncing Balls

> **MATERIALS:** one high-bouncing ball (ping-pong, super ball, golf ball, etc.),
> centimeter measuring tape, graph paper

Attach the centimeter tape to a wall, or have one person hold it so zero
touches the ground. You will be measuring the heights of the first
three bounces.

1. Complete the table. From a height A of 2 meters, drop the ball onto a
   hard surface and record the height of the first three bounces. Repeat
   this five times from this height.

Height	A	B	C	D
Trial Number	Bounce 0	Bounce 1	Bounce 2	Bounce 3
1	200 cm			
2	200 cm			
3	200 cm			
4	200 cm			
5	200 cm			
Mean	200 cm			

2. Use the data from the bottom line of the table to graph the results.
   What are the two variables in this situation? Which is the independent
   variable? the dependent variable?

   _____

   _____

3. Describe the graph. Are the quantities directly related or inversely
   related? Is the relationship linear? Explain.

   _____

   _____

4. Estimate what percent of the previous bounce height that each
   successive bounce height reaches.

   _____

5. Can you write an equation that shows the relationship between the two
   quantities? Show and explain your work.

   _____

   _____

Activity 20: Modeling Polynomial Subtraction

MATERIALS: pencil, algebra tiles

You can use algebra tiles to subtract polynomials.

Example $(2x^2 + 3x + 4) - (x^2 + 3)$

Model the first expression
with algebra tiles.

Remove tiles representing
the second expression. Take
away one x^2 and 3 units.

, or $x^2 + 3x + 1$

$(2x^2 + 3x + 4) - (x^2 + 3) = x^2 + 3x + 1$

Show the first polynomial using algebra tiles. Take away the second
polynomial. Write the polynomial for the tiles that are left.
Sketch your models in the spaces provided.

1. $(4x^2 + 3x + 6) - (x^2 + x + 1)$

2. $(8x + 2) - (2x + 2)$

Resulting polynomial: _____

Resulting polynomial: _____

3. $(2x^2 + 4) - (2x^2 + 3)$

4. $(3x^2 + 4x + 5) - (2x^2 + 2x + 2)$

Resulting polynomial: _____

Resulting polynomial: _____

5. $(4x^2 + 6) - (2x^2 + 1)$

6. $(2x^2 + 3x + 7) - (2x^2 + 3x + 6)$

Resulting polynomial: _____

Resulting polynomial: _____

Activity 21: Multiplying Binomials

MATERIALS: Algebra tiles

You can use algebra tiles to model the multiplication of binomials.
Example $(x - 5)(x - 2)$

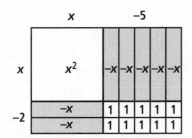

For example, the large square white tile above represents $x \cdot x$, or x^2.
Each of the 5 vertical shaded rectangles represents $-x$. Together they
signify $-5x$. Similarly, the 2 horizontal shaded tiles signify $-2x$. The 10 small
squares represent the number $-2 \cdot -5$, or 10. The arrangement above
represents the equation

$$(x - 5)(x - 2) = x^2 - 7x + 10.$$

1. Multiply $x - 3$ by $x + 2$. Write $x - 3$ across the top of your diagram
   and $x + 2$ down the left side. Start with a large square tile.
   Is it shaded? _____

2. How many long rectangular tiles do you put to the right of the
   large square? _____ Are they shaded? _____

3. How many long rectangular tiles do you put underneath the
   large square? _____ Are they shaded? _____

4. Fill out the rest of the large rectangle with small square tiles. How
   many do you use? _____ Are they shaded? _____

5. From your tile arrangement, the product of $x - 3$ by $x + 2$ is

   _____.

Set up an arrangement of algebra tiles for each multiplication. List the tiles
you use by shape and shading. Write the product.

6. $(x - 5)(x - 1)$ _____

7. $(x + 3)(-x + 2)$ _____

8. $(x - 4)(x + 2)$ _____

9. $(2x + 3)(x - 1)$ _____

Activity 22: Special Products
• •

> **MATERIALS:** cardboard, number tiles

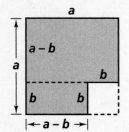
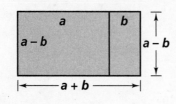

You can demonstrate that $a^2 - b^2 = (a + b)(a - b)$ using pieces of cardboard.

Choose two measurements, a and b, with $a > b$. Cut out a square each of whose sides has length a. From the lower right-hand corner, remove a square with sides of length b, as shown at the left above. The area of the shaded region at the left is the area of the large square, a^2, minus the area of the small cut-out square, b^2.

Now cut along the dotted line shown. When the smaller rectangle is shifted so that it occupies the position shown at the right above, the two rectangles form a single long rectangle with length $a + b$ and width $a - b$. The shaded area at the right is therefore $(a + b)(a - b)$. Thus

$$a^2 - b^2 = (a + b)(a - b)$$

1. To factor $4x^2 - 9$, what do you label a side of the large square? _____. What do you label a side of the small square to be cut out? _____

2. Cut the small square out. What is the area of the remaining piece?_____

3. Cut the remaining piece into two rectangles. What are the areas of the two rectangles? _____

4. Put the two rectangles together so that their equal sides match up.

   What are the dimensions of the large rectangle you get? _____

   What is the area of this large rectangle? _____

Factor, using the cardboard rectangles.

5. $16z^2 - 25$ _____

6. $v^2 - 81w^2$ _____

7. $9 - 49u^2$ _____

8. $-36r^2 + 121q^2$ _____

9. $x^6 - 64y^2$ _____

10. $-49a^2 + 144b^4$ _____

Activity 23: Completing the Square

•••

MATERIALS: Algebra tiles

In this activity, you will complete the square using algebra tiles.

To illustrate the method, let's complete $x^2 - 6x$ to a perfect square by adding a constant. As before, a large square tile, white or shaded, represents the term x^2 or $-x^2$. Similarly, a long rectangular tile represents x or $-x$, and you think of its short side as having length 1.

Model the given expression with the tiles, as shown below. Split the 6 long rectangles into two equal groups to create an open square at the lower right.

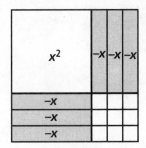

To "complete the square," you need 9 small unit square tiles. Add these to the array of tiles. You now have a model for the expression

$$x^2 - 6x + 9,$$

which is the completed square $(x - 3)^2$.

1. To use the method outlined above for the expression $x^2 + 10x$, how many large square tiles do you use? _____

   How many long rectangular tiles do you use? _____

   Are they shaded? _____

2. How do you split up the long rectangular tiles? _____

3. How many small square tiles do you need to complete the square? _____

4. The completed square is _____ .

Complete the square, using algebra tiles as described above.

5. $x^2 - 14x$ _____   6. $x^2 + 12x$ _____

7. $x^2 + 8x$ _____   8. $x^2 - 16x$ _____

9. $x^2 - 18x$ _____   10. $x^2 + 2x$ _____

Activity 24: Quadratic Solutions

•••

MATERIALS: calculator, graph paper, paper clips

On a sheet of graph paper, draw a Cartesian coordinate system and label the x and y axes with units of 1, 2, . . ., etc., as shown. Bend a paper clip and reshape it in the exact form of the parabola shown.

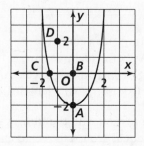

The general equation for the parabola (quadratic equation) is:

$$y = ax^2 + bx + c.$$

All real solutions equal the points on the parabola that intersect the x-axis.

1. Place the bottom of the parabolic paper clip at point A as shown. What is the value of y when x = 0? _____

2. Without moving the paper clip, how many solutions are there for x? _____ What are their values when y = 0? _____

3. Now move the parabolic paper clip up until the bottom is at B. What is the value of y when x = 0? _____

4. How many solutions are there for x and what are their values when y = 0? _____

5. Now move the parabolic paper clip to the left from point B to C. How many solutions are there for x and what are their values when y = 0? _____

6. What is the value of y when x = 0? _____

7. Finally, move the parabolic paper clip up so that the bottom is at point D. Is there any value of x for which y equals zero? _____

8. How many real solutions are there for x now? _____

The solutions of the quadratic equation for x are obtained by setting y = 0 which gives two solutions:

$$x = \frac{-b \pm \sqrt{b^2 - 4ac}}{2a}$$

If $b^2 - 4ac > 0$, then a quadratic equation has two real solutions.
If $b^2 - 4ac = 0$, then it has one real solution.

9. In Exercise 2 above, is $(b^2 - 4ac)$ greater, equal, or less than zero? _____
   Why? _____

10. In Exercise 3 above, is $(b^2 - 4ac)$ greater, equal, or less than zero? _____
    Why? _____

Activity 25: Latitude and Temperature

MATERIALS: world almanac, current newspaper, graph paper

1. Use an almanac or reference book to find the latitudes of some of the world's major cities. Use the cities below, your city, *and at least 10 other*s. You may round to the nearest degree. (Since there are 60 minutes in 1 degree, 45° 29' rounds down to 45°, and 45° 30' rounds up to 46°).

Cities	Latitude	Low Temperature
Ho Chi Minh City, Vietnam	Latitude 11° N	
Sydney, Australia	Latitude 34° S	
Moscow, Russia	Latitude 55° N	

2. In a current newspaper or a search engine on the web, find yesterday's low temperature for each city and complete the table above.

3. Make a scatter plot of your data with latitude on the x-axis and temperature on the y-axis. (Consider south latitudes as negative. For example, for 20° S, use −20.)

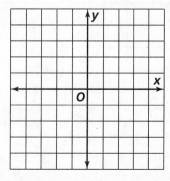

4. What kind of function best describes the relationship between latitude and low temperature?

_____

Activity 26: The Pythagorean Theorem

MATERIALS: graph paper, scissors

Cut out 13 squares from graph paper, with these dimensions.

3×3	6×6	9×9	12×12
4×4	7×7	10×10	13×13
5×5	8×8	11×11	14×14
		15×15	

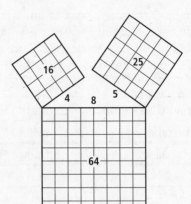

Using three squares at a time, arrange them to form a triangle as shown.

1. Determine the type of triangle formed in each case. Keep track of your results in the table below. Form at least ten triangles using the thirteen squares.

Length of the side of each square			Area of each square			Type of Triangle
a	b	c	a^2	b^2	c^2	
4	5	8	16	25	64	Obtuse

2. Focus on cases where a *right* triangle was formed. Write a conjecture about the areas of the squares that form right triangles.
   Problem-Solving Tip: Look for a pattern.

_____

_____

_____

_____

Activity 27: Geoboard Challenges

....

MATERIALS: geoboard, rubber band

Use a geoboard and rubber band to construct right triangles with the given dimensions. Fill in any missing dimensions. Then draw them on the dot paper.

1. Legs: 1 unit

   Hypotenuse: _____ units

   . . . . .
   . . . . .
   . . . . .
   . . . . .
   . . . . .

2. Legs: $\sqrt{2}$ units

   Hypotenuse: _____ units

   . . . . . .
   . . . . . .
   . . . . . .
   . . . . . .
   . . . . . .

3. Legs 2 units

   Hypotenuse: _____ units

   . . . . .
   . . . . .
   . . . . .
   . . . . .
   . . . . .

4. Legs: $2\sqrt{2}$ units

   Hypotenuse: _____ units

   . . . . . .
   . . . . . .
   . . . . . .
   . . . . . .
   . . . . . .

5. Legs: ____ units
   (Assume the two legs are equal)

   Hypotenuse: $4\sqrt{2}$ units

   . . . . .
   . . . . .
   . . . . .
   . . . . .
   . . . . .

6. Legs: $\sqrt{5}$ units

   Hypotenuse: _____ units

   . . . . . .
   . . . . . .
   . . . . . .
   . . . . . .
   . . . . . .

Activity 28: Indirect Measurement

> **MATERIALS:** protractor, paper clip, straw, calculator

You have used a protractor to measure angles on paper. You can also use a protractor to measure angles so that you can calculate lengths that cannot be easily reached. Examples are the height of a tree or even how high your kite is flying. You will need to make an instrument like a transit, a tool surveyors have been using for hundreds of years.

Here is what you will need: a protractor with a hole at the vertex, a drinking straw, and a paper clip.

Open the clip. Push it through the straw and the hole in the protractor.

The straw should rotate around the clip while sliding against the protractor.

To operate your transit, look past the clip through the straw.

To test your transit, you will need: one tree (height unknown).

Follow these steps:

1. Estimate the height of the tree.

2. Pace off 50 feet from the base of the tree.

3. Hold the protractor so the straight end is parallel to the ground. Look through the straw until you see the top of the tree.

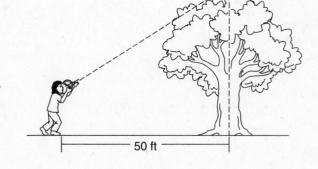

4. Note the angle that the straw makes with the bottom of the protractor.

5. Use the tangent ratio to solve for the height of the tree.

6. How good was your estimate?

7. Several factors in this experiment will cause your result to be a rough estimate. Which ones can you identify?

_____

_____

_____

Use the instrument to measure other heights indirectly.

Activity 29: Travel Rectangles

MATERIALS: pencils, paper

In this activity, you will solve time–rate–distance problems by drawing "travel rectangles."

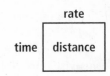

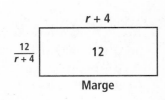

1. Let's illustrate the method to solve the following problem: Alex and Marge bike to work every morning. Marge bikes 4 km per hour faster than Alex and covers 12 km in the same time it takes him to cover 9 km. Find their speeds.

   Choose a variable to represent one of the quantities asked for: Let r = Alex's speed. Then $r + 4$ = Marge's speed. Draw a "travel rectangle" to represent Alex's motion and one to represent Marge's motion. Since distance = rate × time, model the rate and the time by the *length* and *width* of each rectangle, and the distance by its *area*.

   The *times* are the same, so make the widths of the rectangles the same, but make their areas different. Since the area of each rectangle equals length times width, the width of the first rectangle must be $\frac{9}{r}$; the width of the second must be $\frac{12}{r + 4}$.

   a. Write an equation that says that the widths of the two rectangles above are the same and solve of r. _____

   b. What is Alex's speed? _____ What is Marge's speed? _____

2. Snappy Vegetables ships their lettuce to two produce markets, one 135 miles from their farm, the other 195 miles away. The second truck travels 10 mph faster than the first, and their travel times are the same. Let r = the speed of the first truck.

   a. How do you represent the second truck's speed? _____

   b. Which dimension of the two rectangles is the same? _____ Set up an equation that expresses this fact. _____
   Solve the equation for r. What are the speeds?_____

3. Yesterday Delivery Service has two vans. One travels a certain route at 65 km/h; the other covers the same route at 60 km/h. The first van's travel time is 1 hour less than the second van's time. Let t = the second van's travel time.

   a. How do you represent the first van's time? _____

   b. What two expressions do you get for the areas (distances) of the two rectangles? _____

   c. Write an equation that expresses the equality of these areas.
   _____ Solve the equation for t.

   d. What are the two times? _____

Activity 30: Permutations and Combinations

· ·

MATERIALS: colored counters (optional); paper

1. Divide into groups of four. (If there are extra people, they can work to help direct the group or to record the group's findings. Alternately, colored counters can be used in place of people.) The purpose of this activity is to explore a way of counting combinations.

2. Stand in a line. Write down the order in which you are standing.
   _____

3. Now perform a permutation. How many possible permutations are there? _____

4. Your goal is to personally experience half of the total number of permutations. Record the ones you try on a separate sheet of paper.

5. Now choose your favorite permutation, but split the line into two groups of two people. Stand apart so that there is a space between the two groups. Let's call one group the Blue group, the other the Green group. We will count the number of ways of choosing two items from a group of four.

6. Arrange the groups in all possible permutations. The only rule is that you cannot leave your color group and the groups cannot switch places! Record your permutations and draw a line to separate the two groups. For example:

   CA | BD

7. How many permutations are there within each group? _____

8. How many possible permutations are there if the groups aren't allowed to mix? _____

9. Pretend that a very peculiar stranger is observing this. This stranger cannot recognize you as individuals, but sees only the color of the group you are in. So you might see the permutation of C A | B D, but the stranger sees only Blue Blue | Green Green, say. Of all the different permutations you recorded in Exercise 6 above, how many different permutations will the stranger see? _____

10. Choose two items from your group of four. Order is no longer important, so all additional permutations look the same. Your answer to Exercise 3 is the total number of permutations, but your answer to Exercise 8 is the number of those permutations which look the same, once we have selected two items.
    Divide your answer to Exercise 3 by your answer to Exercise 8. _____

11. Compute $_4C_2$. Is this the same as Exercise 10? _____

12. If time remains, repeat the experiment to investigate $_4C_1$ or $_4C_3$.

Activity 31: Algebraic Expressions

MATERIALS: algebra tiles, graphing calculator or graph paper

Compare these two expressions using algebra tiles or graphs.

$x^2 - 2x + 3$

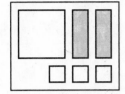

$-5x + 3x^2 + 3x - 2x^2 + 3$

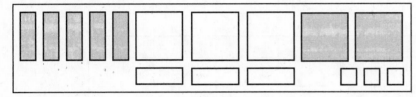

Use one or both of Exercises 1 and 2 to compare the expressions. Then do
Exercise 3.

1. Use the rules for working with algebra tiles to simplify the
   second expression. What do you notice?

   _____

   _____

   _____

2. Graph the functions $y = x^2 - 2x + 3$ and $y = -5x + 3x^2 - 2x^2 + 3$ on a
   graphing calculator or a coordinate plane. What do you notice?

   _____

   _____

3. Make a conjecture about how these two expressions are related.
   Support your conjecture.

   _____

   _____

   _____

Activity 32: It's a Toss-Up

> **MATERIALS:** coin

Toss a coin 12 times. Make a check (✔) beside "Tails" each time a tail appears and beside "Heads" each time a head appears. To generate the next row, write the total number of tails (or heads) you have obtained so far over the total number of tosses. Find the percent by dividing the numerator by the denominator and multiplying the result by 100. Round to the nearest whole number.

Tosses	1	2	3	4	5	6	7	8	9	10	11	12
Tails												
Total tails / Total tosses												
Percent of Tails												
Heads												
Total heads / Total tosses												
Percent of Heads												

Make a double line graph to show your results. Use a solid line for the percent of tails obtained. Use a dotted line for the percent of heads.

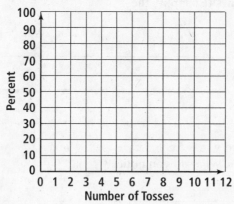

1. Analyze the graph. What do you notice?

_____

_____

2. Predict what happens to the percentage of heads and tails if you increase the number of tosses to 100.

_____

_____

Activity 33: Fun With Functions

MATERIALS: number cube, straightedge, graph paper

Application:

Roll a number cube to get the missing numbers for the following ordered pairs below. Write the numbers in the blanks. After you have generated the required number of ordered pairs, answer Exercises 1–8.

Generate Points of Graph 1.

(,) (,) (,) (,) (,) (,) (,) (,) (,) (,)

Generate Points of Graph 2.

(1,) (2,) (3,) (4,) (5,) (6,) (7,) (8,) (9,) (10,)

Generate Points of Graph 3.

(,1) (,2) (,3) (,4) (,5) (,6) (,7) (,8) (,9) (,10)

Plot the points you generated for each graph on a separate set of axes. Label each graph.

1. Is Graph 1 a function? _____ Why? _____

2. Is Graph 2 a function? _____ Why? _____

3. Is Graph 3 a function? _____ Why? _____

4. What ordered pairs would you have to remove from Graph 1 in order to make it a function?

_____

_____

5. What is the result of performing the Vertical Line Test on a graph of a function? _____

6. What is the result of performing the Vertical Line Test on a graph that is not a function? _____

7. If Graph 2 is called $f(x)$, find:

$f(3) =$ _____ $f(5) =$ _____ $f(1) =$ _____ $f(8) =$ _____ $f(10) =$ _____

$f(6) =$ _____ $f(7) =$ _____ $f(2) =$ _____ $f(9) =$ _____ $f(4) =$ _____

8. If Graph 3 is called $g(x)$, find the value of x for each of the following:

$g(x) = 5; x =$ _____ $g(x) = 4; x =$ _____ $g(x) = 9; x =$ _____

$g(x) = 3; x =$ _____ $g(x) = 10; x =$ _____ $g(x) = 1; x =$ _____

Activity 34: Calculating Slope

MATERIALS: rulers

In this activity you will use a ruler to help you understand the concept of the slope of a line.

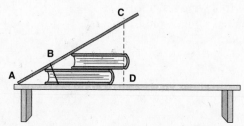

Start by placing a ruler against a small stack of books as shown above. (A rubber band wrapped around the ruler and one of the books, as shown at *B* in the diagram, will hold the ruler in place.)

Choose any point *C* along the ruler and measure the vertical distance *CD* from point *C* to the table top. This is the *rise* of the line represented by the ruler. Next, measure the distance *AD,* from the point where the ruler touches the table top to the point directly below *C*. This is the *run*. The ruler's slope *m* is given by

$$m = \frac{\text{rise}}{\text{run}} = \frac{\text{vertical change}}{\text{horizontal change}}$$

1. Set up the ruler. Measure the distance *CD*. Write down the distance *CD*. _____

2. Measure the distance *AD*. *AD* = _____

3. The slope is "the rise over the run". Find the slope of the ruler. _____

4. If you think of point *A* as the origin of a coordinate system, point *C* has coordinates _____.

5. If point *A* has coordinates (2, 3), the coordinates of *C* are _____.

6. If (*a, b*) represents the answer to Exercise 5, does the fraction $\frac{b-3}{a-2}$ give the slope *m*? _____

7. If *A* has coordinates (4, 1), what are the coordinates of *C*? _____

8. If (*a, b*) represents the answer to Exercise 7, does the fraction $\frac{b-1}{a-4}$ give the slope *m* of the ruler? _____

9. Choose another point *E* on the ruler and calculate the value of *m*. Is it the same? _____

10. Reposition the ruler so that it has a different slant. Choose a point *C* on the ruler, and compute the slope from the measurements *CD* and *AD*. What is the slope? _____

11. Reposition the ruler so that it slants *downward* from left to right. The rise is now *negative*. Find the slope. Is the slope negative? _____

Activity 35: Making a Scatter Plot

MATERIALS: ruler, tape measure

In this activity, you will make a scatter plot to show the relationship between two variable quantities.

To understand the procedure, read the table below, listing the number of minutes several students spent studying for a math test and the scores they achieved on the test. Then look at the *scatter plot* based on this table.

		Students							
	1	**2**	**3**	**4**	**5**	**6**	**7**	**8**	**9**
Study Time (in min.)	20	65	30	90	45	30	80	50	35
Test Score	60	85	70	100	88	77	90	82	80

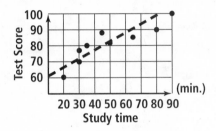

The straight dotted line in the scatter plot shows the *line of best fit* of the given data. It is the line that the data points cluster about. Since the slope of this line is positive, there is a *positive* correlation between study times and tests scores. A negative slope indicates a *negative* correlation between the times and scores. If the data does not cluster about any single line, they are *unrelated*.

Split into groups of between 7 and 9 students. Each group will make a scatter plot of foot length and height (in either centimeters or inches) of the students in the group.

1. With a ruler, measure the length of the right foot of each group member, and with a tape measure, determine the height of each student. Fill in the data you find in the following table.

		Students							
	1	**2**	**3**	**4**	**5**	**6**	**7**	**8**	**9**
Foot Length									
Height									

2. Make a scatter plot of the data: Mark foot lengths on the vertical axis and heights on the horizontal axis. Plot the values you wrote down in the table above.

3. From your scatter plot, is there a correlation between foot length and height? _____ If so, is it positive? _____

4. Measure the height and the circumference of the head of each group member and make a scatter plot of the data. Is there a positive correlation between the data? _____

Activity 36: Wildfires

Most wildfires are caused by lightning. The National Interagency Fire Center uses lightning direction finders (DFs) to find lightning ground strikes, called *flash events*. Two DFs are needed to determine lines to locate the flash event. A computer converts the signals from the DFs to coordinates, using a familiar landmark as the origin.

The map below shows two DF locations in relation to a jump station.

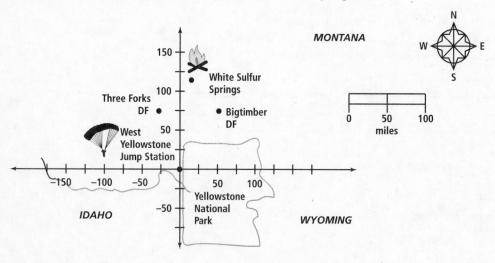

The DFs have detected a flash event near White Sulfur Springs. The computer has determined that the event occurred on the lines $y = 1.17x + 105$ and $y = -1.08x + 130$.

1. Why are two DFs needed to locate the flash event? _____

   _____

2. Find the coordinates where the flash event occurred. Describe how you found the coordinates.

   _____

3. What is the equation of the line from the jump station to the location of the flash event?

   _____

4. In your own words, tell the pilot of a smoke-jumper plane how to get from the jump station to the location of the flash event. Be sure to include both distance and direction in your explanation.

   _____

   _____

Activity 37: Company Logos

MATERIALS: graph paper, magazine or newspaper

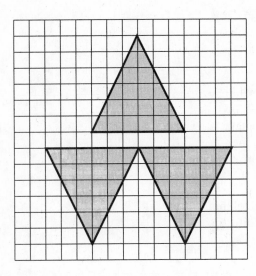

This design is the logo for Addison-Wesley Publishing Company.

1. Choose a point for the origin and draw coordinate axes on the graph. Mark a convenient scale on each axis.

2. Write the equations of the lines that bound the triangular regions. If everyone chooses the same origin, will everyone get the same equations?

_____

_____

3. Use systems of inequalities to describe the triangular regions in the logo. (Hint: You will need three inequalities to describe each region.)

_____

_____

_____

4. Look through your magazine or newspaper. Find a company design or logo, and then draw it on graph paper using only straight lines.

5. Write equations for the lines in your drawing.

6. Use systems of inequalities to describe the regions in your drawing.

Activity 38: Adding Matrices

MATERIALS: transparencies; color transparency pens (blue/green/red)

In this activity you will work with a partner to understand addition of matrices. You will each build your own matrix and then add them together.

A. Building a Matrix

Color will be used to represent the rows of your matrix. That is, everything in the same row of your matrix must be the same color. The first row will be red, the second row green, and the third row blue. Similarly, shapes will be used to represent the columns of your matrix. So everything in the same column must have the same shape. For now we will build a matrix with only three columns.

On the paper, draw a matrix placing a square in each row of the first column, a circle in each row of the second, and a triangle in each row of the third (do not forget to change colors with rows).

1. In which row would you find a blue triangle? _____

2. In which column would you find a blue triangle? _____

3. Would a green circle be out of place in the second row, third column? _____

4. Where would you put a red square? _____

Now draw a number of shapes in each matrix position using the color/row, shape/column convention. For instance, you can have 2 green circles in the second row and second column. Your partner should do the same.

B. Adding Matrices

5. In the space below, write the number of objects you put in each position. The position of the number you write down should correspond to the position of the objects in your matrix.

Your matrix   Partner's matrix

6. Write down your partner's numbers.

7. Add the objects in your partner's matrix to your own, being careful not to mix colors or shapes. Count the number of items in each position and write them to the right.

Activity 39: Matrix "Eggsperiment"

MATERIALS: empty egg cartons, pennies, tape

Make the matrices.

- Use scissors to divide the cartons into 2 by 1, 2 by 2, and 2 by 3 sections.

- Decide each section's orientation to obtain a matrix. For instance, a 2 by 3 section can give you 2×3 matrix or 3×2 matrix.

- Place anywhere from 0 to 5 pennies in each space for every matrix. Leave some of the spaces empty.

Activity Directions

The number of pennies in each position of carton represents the value of that entry in the matrix. Pick a partner and compare your matrices to your classmates' matrices. Decide whether or not you can add your matrix to another matrix, or multiply your matrix with another matrix.

Add or multiply your matrix with your partner's to create the new resulting matrix. Decide whether or not a different size matrix or additional pennies are required. You can use tape to put smaller matrices together and create larger ones.

1. Which size matrices could be added to your matrix?

_____

_____

2. Which size matrices could be multiplied with your matrix? Does the way the carton was orientated make a difference?

_____

_____

3. How do you find the size of a matrix resulting from the multiplication of two matrices? Explain by giving an example.

_____

_____

4. Is the size of the product of two matrices always different from the original matrices? Explain by giving an example.

_____

_____

5. Is the size of the sum of two matrices always the same as the original matrices? _____

Activity 40: Building a Parabola

· ·

> **MATERIALS:** compass

Using the vertically lined paper below and a compass, you can graph a parabola. Follow these steps:

1. In the space provided below, draw a directrix. The directrix should be perpendicular to the vertical lines and should be pretty close to the bottom of the page. This will give you enough room for the parabola.

2. Above the directrix, draw a focus. Pick a focus on the center line so that your graph will be centered on the page.

3. Go to the vertical line to the immediate left of the focus. Using your compass, find the spot on that line which is the same distance from the focus as it is from the directrix. When you have done this, find a spot on the next vertical line to the left which is equidistant from the focus and the directrix. Repeat this process until you have plotted five points to the left of the focus.

4. Repeat Step 3, but starting with the line to the immediate right of the focus. Plot a total of five points to the right of the focus.

5. You should have a parabola! Connect the dots.

Activity 41: Calculating Gravity

MATERIALS: stopwatch, coin or other small object, meterstick

To find the value of g in the free-fall equation $h(t) = -\frac{1}{2}gt^2 + v_0t + h_0$, you can perform a simple experiment. In this equation, v_o is the initial velocity and h_0 is the initial height. If you drop the ball without using any force, then the initial velocity $v_0 = 0$. Suppose the coordinate system is placed so the height of the graph is 0. The $h(t)$ on the left-hand-side is 0 when the object hits the ground.

1. Drop an object with very little wind resistance, such as a coin, from several different heights. Use your stopwatch to measure the time it takes to fall. Record your results in the table.

Height	Time

2. Take the values for time and height from your first experiment. By substituting these values for t and h_0 into $0 = -\frac{1}{2}gt^2 + v_0t + h_0$, you can write an equation in which the only unknown is g. Solve this equation for g.

    _____

3. Repeat Exercise 2 using your time and height data for each experiment. Then average your values for g. How close is your experimental value to the theoretical value 9.8m/s^2 or 32 ft/s^2?

    _____

4. Describe some possible sources of error in your experiment. Given these, would you expect your experimental value for g to be larger or smaller than the theoretical value? Explain.

    _____

    _____

    _____

Activity 42: Powers of *i*

MATERIALS: toothpick with a colored tip

With a partner, explore the powers of *i* using a toothpick.

Representing Powers of *i*

Powers of *i* can be represented by rotating a toothpick with a colored tip. A toothpick represents 1 (or i^0)with the colored tip going towards the right ⟹. Positive powers are represented by rotating to the left counter-clockwise (CCW) by 90° for each positive power. For example, i^1 is ⤊, i^2 is ⟸, i^3 is ⤋, i^4 is ⟹, which is the same as i^0 (or 1). Negative powers are represented by rotating to the right clockwise (CW) by 90° for each negative power. For example, i^{-1} is ⤋, i^{-2} is ⟸, i^{-3} is ⤊, and i^{-4} is ⟹, which is the same as i^0 (= 1). Represent each of the following powers of *i* by rotating the toothpick from the initial position with the tip going rightward ⟹. Higher powers of *i* are equivalent to basic powers of *i* ($i^0 = 1, i^1 = i, i^2 = -1$, or $i^3 = -i$) when the toothpick has the same orientation. For example, $i^5 = i$.

Student 1:   **1.** $i^9 =$ _____   Student 2:   **1.** $i^{13} =$ _____

              2. $i^{16} =$ _____   **2.** $i^{19} =$ _____

              3. $i^{-9} =$ _____   **3.** $-i^{-3} =$ _____

Representing Negative Sign with Powers of *i*

A negative value can be represented by flipping the toothpick so that the colored tip points in the opposite direction. In this manner −1 is done by flipping from 1 ⟹ to get −1 ⟸, and −*i* is done by flipping from *i* ⤊ to get −*i* ⤋. Similarly, $-i^5$ is done by first rotating left (CCW) five times to get *i* ⤊, and then flipping over to give a final result of −*i* ⤋. (**Try It!**) Represent each of the following powers of *i* by rotating the toothpick from the initial position, and then flipping, if a negative sign is applied. Convert to the equivalent basic value (1, *i*, −1, or −*i*).

Student 1:   **4.** $i^{-1} =$ _____   Student 2:   **4.** $-i^1 =$ _____

              5. $-i^2 =$ _____   **5.** $i^{-2} =$ _____

              6. $-i^{-9} =$ _____   **6.** $-i^{17} =$ _____

Activity 42: Powers of *i* (continued)
••

Multiplying Powers of *i*

To represent a power of *i*, we always started with the toothpick at $1 \Rightarrow$. When multiplying two powers of *i*, the same process is used (rotating and flipping) but instead, the final position for the first power is used as the starting point for the second power. In this manner, $(i^5)(-i^3)$ is done by first rotating left (CCW) five times to get $i \Uparrow$, then using this as the starting point for $(-i^3)$ which involves rotating left three more times to get $1 \Rightarrow$, and then flipping over 180° to give a final result of $-1 \Leftarrow$. (**Try It!**) Represent each of the following powers of *i* by rotating and flipping the toothpick from the initial position for the first factor, and then rotating and flipping the toothpick from this position for the second factor. Convert to the equivalent basic value $(1, i, -1, \text{ or } -i)$.

Student 1:   **7.** $(i^3)(i^7) =$ _____

8. $(i^6)(i^{-7}) =$ _____

9. $(-i^7)(i^4) =$ _____

10. $(i^{-6})(-i^7) =$ _____

Student 2:   **7.** $(i^5)(i^9) =$ _____

8. $(i^3)(i^{-6}) =$ _____

9. $(i^5)(-i^8) =$ _____

10. $(-i^2)(i^{-9}) =$ _____

Activity 43: Dividing Polynomials

MATERIALS: algebra tiles

You can make and use algebra tiles like those shown below to model dividing with polynomials.

x^2 $-x^2$ x $-x$ 1 -1

Example 1: $\dfrac{x^2 + 4x + 4}{x + 2} = x + 2$

Arrange the tiles in a rectangular shape so that one side represents the divisor and the whole shape represents the dividend. Then the other side will show the quotient.

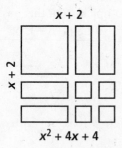

$x + 2$

$x + 2$

$x^2 + 4x + 4$

Example 2: $\dfrac{x^2 - 9}{x + 3} = x - 3$

Tiles representing both positive and negative expressions must be used. To show the quotient, you will use a white block for x^2 and 9 shaded unit tiles for -9. To undo the adding of 3 white x-tiles for the divisor, you must add 3 shaded x-tiles when showing the dividend.

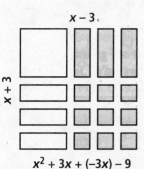

$x - 3$

$x + 3$

$x^2 + 3x + (-3x) - 9$

Example 3: $\dfrac{x^2 + 2x - 12}{x - 3} = x + 5 + \dfrac{3}{x - 3}$

If there are too many or too few single tiles to form a rectangle, then write the quotient plus or minus the remainder over the divisor.

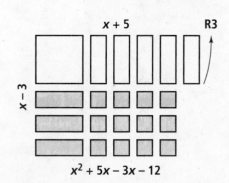

$x + 5$ R3

$x - 3$

$x^2 + 5x - 3x - 12$

Use your tiles to model each of the following: Draw the models on a separate sheet of paper and write the quotient.

1. $\dfrac{x^2 + 5x + 6}{x + 2}$ _____

2. $\dfrac{x^2 + x - 6}{x + 3}$ _____

3. $\dfrac{x^2 - 6x + 9}{x - 3}$ _____

4. $\dfrac{x^2 - 25}{x + 5}$ _____

5. $\dfrac{x^2 + 2x - 9}{x - 2}$ _____

6. $\dfrac{x^2 + 5x - 9}{x - 2}$ _____

Activity 44: Roots and Degrees

MATERIALS: cardboard, string, pen, ruler, pencil

Draw a horizontal and a vertical axis on a square piece of cardboard so that the origin is approximately in the center. You should use a ruler to be sure the lines are straight and at right angles. We will use the string to graph polynomials. When you have a graph you like, you might want to sketch it on a separate sheet of paper to help you answer some of the questions.

A. Third Degree Polynomials

1. How many real roots can a third degree polynomial have? _____

Remember, a root occurs where the graph crosses the *x*-axis.

2. By laying the string on the cardboard, graph a third degree polynomial with three roots. How many hills and valleys are there? _____

3. The left and right ends of a third degree polynomial always point in opposite directions. (If one end points up, the other points down.) Keeping this in mind, use the string to graph a third degree polynomial with two roots. Now how many hills and valleys are there? _____

4. Graph a third degree polynomial with one root so that there are no hills or valleys.

5. Graph a third degree polynomial with one root so that there is one hill and one valley.

B. Fifth Degree Polynomials

6. Graph a fifth degree polynomial with five roots. How many hills and valleys does it have? _____

7. Graph a fifth degree polynomial with three roots. Does it look like any of the graphs you did for part A? _____

8. Graph a fifth degree polynomial with 1 root. Which graph from part A does it look like? _____

C. Fourth Degree Polynomials

Remember that for fourth degree polynomials, both ends of the graph point in the same direction.

9. Graph a fourth degree polynomial with four roots. How many hills and valleys are there? _____

10. Graph a fourth degree polynomial with three roots. How does it differ from your graph in Exercise 2? _____

Activity 45: Square Roots

•••

> **MATERIALS:** scissors, construction paper, ruler

This activity shows how to represent square roots as physical objects.

1. Use a ruler to draw two squares on a sheet of construction paper.
    One square should have sides 2 inches long and the other 3 inches long.
    Cut these squares out of the paper.

    a. What is the area of each square? _____
        Write these areas on the squares.

    b. The length of the sides of each square represents the square root
        of the number you have written on the squares. Use a radical
        expression to represent the length of the side of each square.

        _____

2. Without showing your partner, cut out a square with an unusual area
    (for example 5.7). Write this area on the square and exchange with
    your partner.

    a. Using only the square and a ruler, calculate the square root of the
        number your partner told you. _____

    b. Cut out a square with the area 16. What is the length of each side?

        _____

3. You know that $\sqrt{4}\,\sqrt{9} = 2 \times 3 = 6$. Cut out a square with sides

    6 inches long. What is this square's area? _____ This should help

    you to understand why $\sqrt{4}\,\sqrt{9}$ is equal to $\sqrt{(4 \times 9)}$.

4. What shape would you use to represent $\sqrt[3]{27}$? _____

5. Cut 4 squares, each with an area of 4. Arrange all 4 of your squares into
    one large square.

    a. What is the area of the big square? _____

    (Note that $\sqrt{(area\ of\ the\ big\ square)}$ is the length of each side of the
    large square in addition to being the area of any of the smaller squares.)

    b. Express the area of any of the smaller squares as a radical expression.

        _____

Activity 46: It's All in Your Head

MATERIALS: index cards and a dark marker (one per student)

Work as a class to complete the activity. Have each student prepare a list of 5 simple radical equations and answers for the moderator/teacher to use in this activity.

Here are a few simple radical equations you can model:

$x^2 = 25, y^3 + 1 = 9, x^2 - 4 = 0$

Directions

Teams compete against each other in this mental math game for the title of "Most Radical."

- Divide the class into teams by rows. Each team member in the row is numbered.

- Each student gets a marker and index card.

- The Number Ones on each team begin.

- From the list the teacher/moderator reads a radical equation or writes it on the board.

- Students solve the equation mentally. They do not show any work but write their answer on their index card large enough to be easily seen by the moderator. Team members may not help each other.

- After approximately five seconds the teacher/moderator says "Answers." The students who are Number Ones show their answers.

- Each student who answers correctly earns a point for their team.

- Play continues with the students who are Number Twos, Number Threes, and so on.

Discussion

- Students discuss the methods they used to solve the radical equations.

Activity 47: A Tower of Powers

MATERIALS: cardboard or paper, compass

The Tower of Hanoi is a puzzle in which 8 disks, each with a different diameter, are piled in order of size on one of three rods. The goal is to move the tower from one rod to another. Only one disk may be moved at a time and no disk may be placed on a smaller one. What is the fewest number of moves it will take?

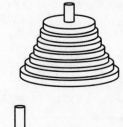
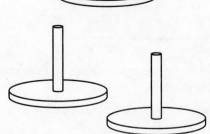

You can experiment with a homemade Tower of Hanoi constructed by drawing and cutting out 8 circles each with a larger diameter.

1. To get started, try solving the puzzle with 1, 2, 3, 4, and 5 disks. Fill in the table.

disks	1	2	3	4	5
moves					

Try to derive a formula for the number of moves required for *d* disks. Look for a pattern in the solutions. Use the following as clues.

2. List the differences between each number of moves and the preceding number of moves. _____

3. Express each of the answers in Exercise 2 as a power of 2.

   _____

4. Express the number of moves using Exercise 3.

   _____

5. Write a formula for the number of moves.
   Let d = the number of disks.
   Let m = the number of moves.

   _____

6. Use the formula to complete the table.

d	6	7	8
m			

   Graph the results for d = 1 through 7.

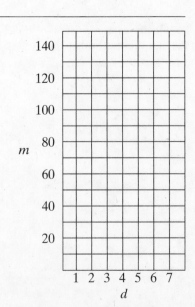

Activity 48: How Loud?

A rock band plays various venues, each having different noise level limits. Use the formula $L = 10 \log \frac{I}{I_0}$ for the following problems that the band must consider. I is the intensity level of the sound and I_0 is a constant.

The first stop on the tour is a small indoor hall having a 105 decibel limit. Use the noise limit formula to answer the following exercises.

1. If the band plays at an intensity level $10^{10} I_0$, will this be acceptable?

_____

2. If the band plays louder at an intensity $10^{11} I_0$, will this be acceptable?

_____

3. Find the maximum intensity at which the band can play at this hall.

_____

The second show is at a small outdoor theater near a residential district having a 120 decibel limit.

4. If the band plays at an intensity $1.58 \times 10^{11} I_0$, how many

decibels is this? _____

5. Is an intensity level $7.94 \times 10^{11} I_0$ acceptable?_____

6. Find the maximum intensity at which the band can play at this theater.

_____

The last stop on the tour is a large amphitheater with a limit of 140 decibels.

7. Can the band play at a level $1.26 \times 10^{14} I_0$ at this show? _____

8. Is $5.01 \times 10^{13} I_0$ an acceptable level? _____

9. Find the maximum intensity allowable at the amphitheater. _____

Activity 49: Inverse Variation

MATERIALS: graph paper, scissors, paste or tape, ruler

In this activity, you will use rectangles to draw the graph of an inverse variation, and use the graph to find values of the variables.

To demonstrate the activity, let's use the inverse variation

$$xy = 30$$

On a sheet of graph paper, outline as many differently shaped rectangles having area 30 as you can, thinking of each grid box on the graph as one square unit. Although the rectangle of length 5 and width 6, for example, has the same shape as the one with length 6 and width 5, make one of each of these. Cut out the rectangles with scissors.

Mark the coordinate axes on another sheet of graph paper, and paste or tape the rectangles onto this other sheet, overlapping, *with the lower left-hand corner of each rectangle at the origin*, as shown.

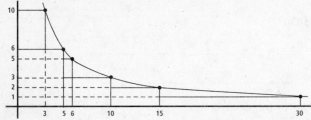

Mark the upper right-hand corner of each rectangle with a dot, and connect these dots with a smooth curve. This is the graph of the inverse variation.

1. Find the value of y when $x = 4$ by putting a ruler on the line $x = 4$ and noting the y-coordinate of the point where the ruler intersects the graph you have drawn. _____

2. Find the value of x when $y = 2.5$ by putting the ruler on the line $y = 2.5$ and noting the x-coordinate of the point where the ruler intersects the graph you have drawn. _____

3. Make rectangles and a graph for the inverse variation $xy = 48$. Use rectangles of heights 2, 3, 4, 6, 8, 16.

4. Use the graph to find the value of y when $x = 2.4$. _____
   What is y when $x = 15$? _____

5. Find the value of x when $y = 5$. _____

   Find the value of x when $y = 9.6$. _____

6. Make rectangles and a graph for the inverse variation $xy = 45$. Use it to fill in the table below.

x	4.5	10		
y			6	2.5

Activity 50: Saving Steps

••

> **MATERIALS:** stopwatch

Complete the tables below. Use a stopwatch to determine how long it takes to complete each answer.

Evaluate: $\dfrac{x^2 - 5x + 6}{x^2 - 4x + 4}$

Table 1

Value of x	Value of $\dfrac{x^2 - 5x + 6}{x^2 - 4x + 4}$	Time in Seconds
5	_____	_____
10	_____	_____
120	_____	_____

Evaluate: $\dfrac{x - 3}{x - 2}$

Table 2

Value of x	Value of $\dfrac{x - 3}{x - 2}$	Time in Seconds
5	_____	_____
10	_____	_____
120	_____	_____

Complete.

1. Compare both tables. What do you notice about the second column in each table? the last column?

   _____

   _____

2. How many separate operations did you do on the calculator for one evaluation in Table 1? in Table 2? _____

3. Simplify: $\dfrac{x^2 - 8x + 7}{x^2 - 7x + 10} \div \dfrac{x^2 - 1}{x^2 - 4x + 4}$ _____

4. How many computational steps can be saved by using the simplified expression in Exercise 3 to evaluate the original expression? _____

••

Activity 51: Drawing Ellipses

MATERIALS: cardboard, thumbtacks, string

1. Push two thumbtacks into a piece of cardboard. Label the thumbtacks F_1 and F_2. Make a loop of string that fits loosely around the thumbtacks. Put your pencil point inside the loop. Keeping the string taut to form a triangle, move your pencil so that a closed curve is drawn. Describe the shape of the curve.

   _____

   _____

2. Choose a point on the curve. Measure the distances from that point to F_1 and F_2. Choose other points and repeat your measurements until you find a pattern. What do you notice? Why does this make sense, given the method you used to draw the ellipse?

   _____

   _____

3. With the thumbtacks different distances apart, draw several ellipses. How does the distance between the thumbtacks affect the shape of the curve?

   _____

   _____

4. Using a string with a different length, draw more ellipses. How does the length of the string affect the ellipse?

   _____

   _____

5. If F_1 and F_2 coincide, what happens to the shape of the ellipse?

   _____

   _____

Activity 52: Conic Sections

· ·

> **MATERIALS:** cardboard, marking pen, construction paper, compass, scissors, tape

1. Use a compass to draw a circle. Cut out the circle and cut a slit from its
    outside to its center. Roll up the circle to make a right cone as shown
    and fasten it with tape.

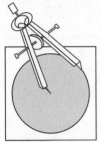  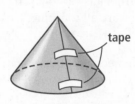

2. Using a sheet of cardboard to represent a plane, find a way to
    cut the cone with a plane so that the intersecting curve is a circle.
    With your marking pen, sketch the circle on your cone. Describe the
    relationship between the plane and the cone.

    _____

    _____

    _____

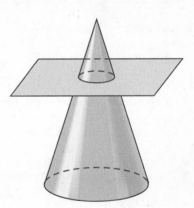

3. How might the plane intersect the cone for the intersecting curve
    to be an ellipse? A parabola?

    _____

    _____

4. Look for other shapes that you can generate by cutting a cone with
    a plane. Describe or illustrate these figures and explain how they can
    be formed.

    _____

    _____

5. Explain why the ellipse, circle, parabola, and hyperbola are known as
    conic sections.

    _____

    _____

Activity 53: Arithmetic Sequences

••

> **MATERIALS:** counters

The odd numbers 1, 3, 5, 7, . . . form an arithmetic sequence. (What is the value of d—the difference between successive terms—for this sequence?) Let's just consider the first four terms for now.

1. What is the sum of the first four terms? _____

2. Take the number of counters from answer to Exercise 1 and arrange the counters in a square so they are all touching. This grid will form the base of a pyramid.

3. In the space wherever four counters meet, place another counter on top of each of these spaces to create the next level of the pyramid.

   How many counters are there on this new level? _____

4. Continue in this manner until you reach the top of the pyramid.

   How many levels are there? _____

5. Notice that there is one level for each term of our sequence. Let's call the top level, Level 1. Write the number of counters on each level:

   _____

6. Now write the sum of the first term of the sequence, the sum of the first two terms , the sum of the first three terms, and the sum of all four terms.

   What do you notice? _____

7. Notice that the square of each level number forms the sequence 1, 4, 9, 16 ($1^2, 2^2, 3^2, 4^2$). What does this tell you about the sum of the first n odd numbers?

   _____

8. Suppose we were going to build a bigger pyramid. How many counters would be on

   Level 5? _____

   Level 7? _____

   Level 100? _____

9. What is the next term in the sequence $-1, -4, -7, . . .$? _____

10. What is the fifth term in the sequence 5, 9, 13, . . . ? _____

Activity 54: Find the Sum of a Sequence

MATERIALS: construction paper, scissors

The nth term of an arithmetic sequence is given by the formula
$$a_n = a_1 + (n - 1) \cdot d.$$

The sum of the first n terms of an arithmetic series is given by the formula
$$S_n = \left(\frac{n}{2}\right) \cdot (a_1 + a_n).$$

Cut out six markers of any shape. We will use these to represent terms of a series. Choose an initial value a_1 for the series and write this on a marker. Now choose a value for d, the difference between successive terms in the sequence. On another marker, write the value of $a_1 + d$. Write the next four terms of the sequence on the remaining markers, and lay out all six markers in order.

Now, rearrange the markers into pairs so that the first and last terms, the second and fifth terms, and the third and fourth terms are together.

1. What is the sum of each pair? _____

2. Why does each pair have the same sum?
   (Hint: $a_2 = a_1 + d$ and $a_5 = a_6 - d$. What is $a_2 + a_5$?) _____

The sum of the first 6 terms of a series is the number of pairs multiplied by the sum of each pair.

3. Number of pairs: _____

4. Sum of each pair: _____

5. $S_n =$ _____

What happens if we wish to compute the sum of an odd number of terms? Cut out another marker and write the seventh term of your sequence on it.

6. Rearrange your markers into pairs so that the first and last terms are together, the second and sixth are together, and so on. There is one extra term that does not fit into a pair. Which term is it? _____

7. Now what is the sum of each pair? _____

8. There are still three pairs, but if we multiply the sum of each pair by the number of pairs, we do not get the right sum. What must we add to this result to get the right answer? _____

9. The extra term can be thought of as half of a pair.
   What is two times the extra term? _____

10. Add $\left(\frac{1}{2}\right) \cdot$ (sum of each pair) to the sum of the first three pairs.

    What is the result? _____

Activity 55: Family Probability

MATERIALS: one coin

There are three children in the Petranov family: two girls and one boy.

1. Without doing an experiment or calculation, guess what the probability is of a three-child family having two girls and a boy.

_____

Now you'll find an experimental probability and the theoretical probability and check your guess.

2. Experimental Probability Let one side of a coin represent a girl (G), and the other side a boy (B). You will need to flip the coin three times to represent the children in each family. Simulate data for at least 6 families, and pool the data from your class or group.

Family	1st child	2nd child	3rd child
1			
2			
3			
4			
5			
6			

Find the experimental probability of a three-child family having two girls and a boy.

_____

3. Theoretical Probability List all possible three-child families, such as GBG representing a girl, then a boy, and then a girl. Find the theoretical probability of a three-child family having two girls and a boy.

_____

4. Write a brief paragraph comparing the ease and accuracy of the experimental and theoretical methods. Explain any significant difference between your guess, the experimental probability, and the theoretical probability.

_____

_____

_____

Activity 56: Is Height Normally Distributed?

MATERIALS: measuring tape for each small group

Form small groups. Record each group member's height (in inches).
Combine data from each group so all groups have the same data set
consisting of all class members' heights. Each group should answer the
following exercises.

1. Do you expect this data set to be normally distributed? _____

    _____

2. Calculate the mean and standard deviation of the data set. _____

3. Sketch a bell-shaped distribution of the heights.

4. What is the range of heights within one standard deviation of the mean? _____

5. What percentage of the heights is within the range of heights in Exercise 5? _____

    What percentage of heights would you expect to be within the range in Exercise 5? _____

6. What is the range of heights within two standard deviations of

    the mean? _____

7. What percentage of the heights is within the range of heights in Exercise 7? _____

    What percentage of heights would you expect to be within the range in Exercise 7? _____

8. Calculate and interpret the z-score for a student who is 53" tall. _____

    _____

9. What is the probability of finding a student's height less than 49"? _____

Activity 57: Keeping Track of Time

MATERIALS: clock with a second hand

Watch the second hand on the clock for a minute.

1. Graph the minutes versus position of the second hand for 3 minutes.

2. Is this function periodic? _____

3. If yes, what is the period of the function? _____

4. What happens to the graph if it is shifted over 60 seconds? _____

5. What happens to the graph if it is shifted back 2 minutes? _____

Think about the movement of the hour hand.

6. Graph the hours versus position of the hour hand for 2 days.

7. What is the period of this function? _____

8. How many cycles does the function complete in one day? _____

Imagine an 8-hour clock.

9. Graph the hours versus position of the hour hand for 2 days of an 8-hour clock.

10. What is the period of this function? _____

11. What happens to the graph if it is shifted back 16 hours? _____

12. What would be the period of a 6-hour clock? _____

13. How many cycles would it complete in one day? _____

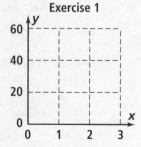

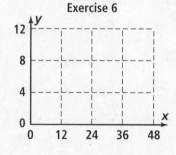

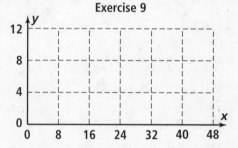

Activity 58: Finding the Measure of an Angle

MATERIALS: metric ruler, protractor, graph paper

In this activity, you will find an angle whose sine, cosine, or tangent is given.

To illustrate, suppose you are given that sin A = 0.34. To find the measure of angle A, choose a convenient length for the hypotenuse, say 10 cm. Since

$$\frac{3.4}{10} = 0.34,$$

you construct a right triangle with a hypotenuse of length 10 cm and with an acute angle A such that the side opposite A has length 3.4 cm.

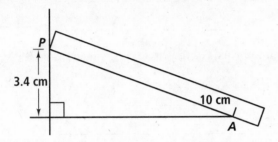

To accomplish this, draw two perpendicular lines on the graph paper. Using a ruler, mark a point P on one of the lines 3.4 cm from their point of intersection. Put the 0 cm marking of a metric ruler at P and rotate the ruler until the 10 cm marking falls on the other perpendicular line. Draw the hypotenuse, guided by the ruler. Label as angle A the acute angle of the triangle not at P.

1. Measure angle A with a protractor. You find that A = _____.

2. Do the same experiment using 20 cm for the hypotenuse and 6.8 cm for the length of the side opposite angle A. Is it still true that sin A = 0.34? _____

3. Measure angle A with the protractor. Is the measure of angle A the same as before?

_____

Find A to the nearest degree, using the method described above.

4. cos A = 0.12 _____   5. sin A = 0.84 _____

6. sin A = 0.72 _____   7. cos A = 0.39 _____

To find A, given the value of tan A, choose two convenient lengths whose quotient is the given value and measure these along the perpendicular lines.

8. tan A = 1.8 _____   9. tan A = 0.51 _____

10. tan A = 0.70 _____   11. tan A = 1.6 _____

Activity 59: Trigonometric Identities

· ·

> **MATERIALS:** scissors, ruler

In Cartesian coordinates draw two circles of 8 cm diameter using a compass. Cut out one circle and fold it in half. Draw a line parallel to this fold at a distance of 2 cm and draw the 30° triangle shown. Cut out two identical 30° triangles. Place one triangle with the longer leg on the *x*-axis of the other circle, as shown. Assume the hypotenuse is one unit in length.

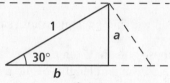

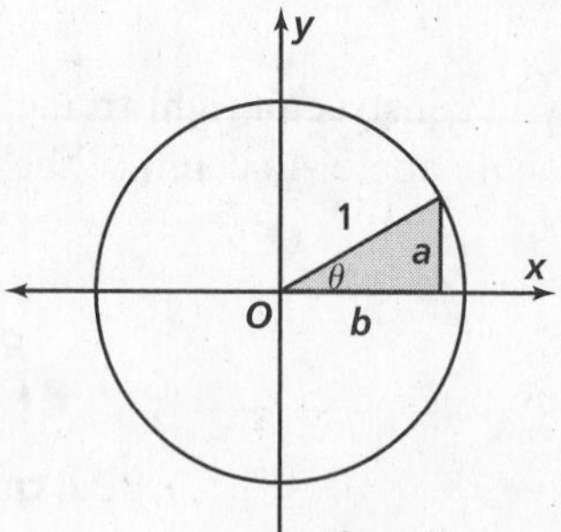

Figure 1

1. The sine of angle θ is _____.

2. The cosine of angle θ is _____.

Next place this triangle with its longer leg on the *y*-axis of the circle, as shown in Figure 3.

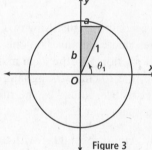

Figure 2

3. The sine of angle θ_1 is now _____.

4. The cosine of angle θ_1 is now _____.

Next, flip the triangle over to the second quadrant, as show in Figure 4.

5. The sine of angle θ_2 is now _____.

6. The cosine of angle θ_2 is now _____.
   (Note that *a* is negative since it is in the negative *x* direction.)

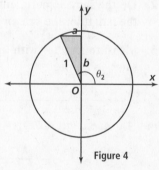

Figure 3

Finally, place the second triangle with the longer leg along the *x*-axis so that both triangles are placed as show in Figure 5.

7. If the cosine of the difference of two angles is given as
   $\cos(\alpha - \beta) = \cos\alpha\cos\beta + \sin\alpha\sin\beta$ find $\cos(\alpha - \beta)$
   by substituting from Exercises 1, 2, 5, and 6 above. Note
   $\alpha = \theta_2$ and $\beta = \theta$.

   Its value is _____.

8. Explain your answer. _____

   _____

   _____

Figure 4

9. If the sine of the difference of two angles is given as
   $\sin(\alpha - \beta) = \sin\alpha\cos\beta - \cos\alpha\sin\beta$ its value is _____.

10. Explain your answer. _____

    _____

    _____

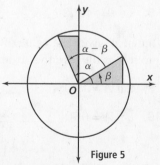

Figure 5

Activity Answers

Activity 1
1-4. Answers may vary.

Activity 2
1. $-3-2 = -5$ **2.** $1 - 4 = -3$ **3.** -15 **4.** -3 **5.** -12 **6.** -3
7. -10 **8.** -2 **9.** -12 **10.** -6 **11.** -12 **12.** 12 **13.** 6
14. -6 **15.** -12 **16.** 12 **17.** -11

Activity 3
1. $3(2 + 5), 3(2) + 3(5)$ **2.** $2, 9$ **3.** $10, 8$ **4.** $12 + 3y$
5. $2n + 6$ **6.** $14x + 21$ **7.** $3x + 3y$ **8.** $8c + 4d$
9. $5p + 45q$ **10.** no **11.** $4(3 + 2)$ or 20 **12.** $5(r + s)$
13. $3(a + 2b)$ **14.** $2(m + 3)$ **15.** $7(2a + b)$
16. $11(u + 4)$ **17.** $3(x + y + z)$ **18.** $7(5v + 1)$
19. $5(3x + 10y)$ **20.** $4(a + 2b + c)$

Activity 4
1. yes; both sides have the same weight **2.** $n = 5$
3. yes; $n + 4 = 9$ **4.** yes; $n + 2 = 7$
5. Take away 2 objects from each side.
6. Take away 13 objects from each side.
7. No, the scale will no longer be balanced .
8. $n + 13 = 21; n + 13 - 13 = 21 - 13; n = 8$

Activity 5
1. $x = -4 + (-x)$ **2.** $x + (-3) = 4$ **3.** $3x + 4 = x + 2$
4. Answers may vary. **5.** Answers may vary.

Activity 6
1–4. Answers may vary.

Activity 7
Yes; Karen can only go on 4 of 9 rides: Spider Web, Haunted
House, Bumper Cars, and Tilt-a-Whirl. She is too young for
Deep 6, even though she is tall enough.

Activity 8
1. true **2.** false; $w > 2$ and $w < 2\frac{1}{16}$ **3.** true
4. false; $w > 2$ and $w < 2\frac{1}{6}$ is equivalent to $2 < w < 2\frac{1}{16}$
5. true **6.** false; $d > 2\frac{1}{2}$ and $d < 2\frac{5}{8}$ represents all diameters
between $2\frac{1}{2}$ and $2\frac{5}{8}$ **7.** true **8.** false; $2 < w < 2\frac{1}{16}$
9. false; $2\frac{1}{2} < d < 2\frac{5}{8}$ **10.** true **11.** Answers may vary.

Activity 9
1. 2 **2.** 2 **3.** 200 pennies **4.** $(200, 100)$

Activity 10
1. $\frac{1}{3}$ **2.** 3 **3–6.** Answers may vary.

7. When a theoretical probability is too difficult to compute,
a simulation can be to generate an experimental probability
for one.

Activity 11
1–4. Answers may vary. **5.** Find the vertical value of the
trend line when the horizontal value is 3.

Activity 12
1. 2 **2.** $4; 8$; twice as many regions as resulting from the
previous fold **3.** $2^n; 2^{10}$ or $1024; 2^{100}$

4. $\frac{1}{2^n}; \frac{1}{2^{10}}; \frac{1}{2^{100}}$ **5.** With every new fold, the number of

regions increases while the portion size decreases.

Activity 13
1–5. Answers may vary.

Activity 14
1. 2 points **2.** point–slope form

Activity 15
1. The weight increases with the number of pages; $y = bx$
2–5. Answers may vary.

Activity 16
1. Answers may vary.
2. 4; assume that the opponent picks the point $(2, 3)$. If you
got lucky and ask if the x coordinate is less than 2 (answer:
no) followed by the question if the x-coordinate is greater
than 2 (answer: no), then you can conclude that the
x-coordinate must be 2. Again if you got very lucky and ask if
the y-coordinate is less than or greater than 3, you should be
able to identify the opponent's point in four questions.
3. When you are relying on luck, the probability of getting
lucky will decrease as n becomes bigger. If you use a strategy
(see solution to exercise 5), then the value of n will also affect
the number of questions needed to identify the point.
4. The inequalities help to narrow the intervals in which
the x- and y-coordinates lie.
5. One strategy includes asking whether the x or y value is
less than 0. This narrows your search by half and should be
continued until the x- and y-coordinates are identified.

Activity Answers (continued)

Activity 17

1a. Yes;

1b. Yes;

1c. No. Answers may vary. Sample: The intersection of two lines is a point, line, or no intersection. It cannot be a region.

1d. Yes;

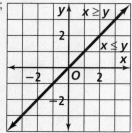

2a. No. Answers may vary. Sample: The graphs of linear inequalities result in regions. So, the intersection of the two cannot be a point.

2b. Yes;

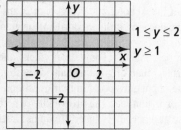

2c. Yes;

2d. Yes;

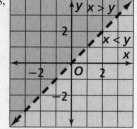

3. Unlike graphs of two linear inequalities, two lines can intersect at a point. Unlike graphs of two linear inequalities, intersection of two lines cannot form a region.
4. Check students' work. **5.** Check students' work.

Activity 18

1–4. Answers may vary. **5.** Approximately 2. Answers will vary with the precision of the measurements.
6. Yes; some students may answer no because of measurement error. **7.** After rounding off, the ratio should be 2.
8. Answers may vary. **9.** 1, 3, 9, 27 **10.** Yes, there is a common ratio of 3. **11.** 2,187 **12.** $A(n) = 3^0$

Activity 19

1–5. Answers may vary.

Activity 20

1. $3x^2 + 2x + 5$ **2.** $6x$ **3.** 1 **4.** $x^2 + 2x + 3$
5. $2x^2 + 5$ **6.** 1

Activity 21

1. no **2.** 3, yes **3.** 2, no **4.** 6, yes **5.** $x^2 + x - 6$
6. 1 unshaded large square tile, 6 shaded long rectangular tiles, 5 unshaded small square tiles; $x^2 - 6x + 5$
7. 1 shaded large square tile, 2 unshaded long rectangular tiles, 3 shaded long rectangular tiles, 6 unshaded small square tiles; $-x^2 - x + 6$
8. 1 unshaded large square tile, 2 unshaded long rectangular tiles, 4 shaded long rectangular tiles, 8 shaded small square tiles; $x^2 - 2x - 8$
9. 2 unshaded large square tile, 3 unshaded long rectangular tiles, 2 shaded long rectangular tiles, 3 shaded small square tiles; $2x^2 + x - 3$

Activity 22

1. $2x$; 3 **2.** $4x^2 - 9$ **3.** $4x^2 - 6x$; $6x - 9$
4. $2x - 3, 2x + 3$; $4x^2 - 9$ **5.** $(4z - 5)(4z + 5)$
6. $(v - 9w)(v + 9w)$ **7.** $(3 - 7u)(3 + 7u)$
8. $(-6r + 11q)(6r + 11q)$ **9.** $(x^3 - 8y)(x^3 + 8y)$
10. $(-7a + 12b^2)(7a + 12b^2)$

Activity 23

1. 1, 10, no **2.** 2 groups of 5 **3.** 25 **4.** $x^2 + 10x + 25$
5. $x^2 - 14x + 49$ **6.** $x^2 + 12x + 36$ **7.** $x^2 + 8x + 16$
8. $x^2 - 16x + 64$ **9.** $x^2 - 18x + 81$ **10.** $x^2 + 2x + 1$

Activity 24

1. -2 **2.** $2; \frac{3}{2}, -\frac{3}{2}$ **3.** 0 **4.** 1; 0 **5.** 1, $-\frac{3}{2}$ **6.** 2 **7.** no

8. none **9.** greater; because the graph has two real solutions
10. equal; because the graph has one real solution

Activity Answers (continued)

Activity 25
1–3. Answers may vary. **4.** linear

Activity 26
1. Answers may vary.
2. Check students' work. For a right triangle, the sum of the areas of the two smaller squares equals the area of the bigger square, or $a^2 + b^2 = c^2$.

Activity 27
1. $\sqrt{2}$ **2.** 2 **3.** $2\sqrt{2}$ **4.** 4 **5.** 4 **6.** $\sqrt{10}$

Activity 28
6. Answers may vary. **7.** Answers may include the following response: accuracy of measuring the distance from the tree, accounting for students' height, keeping the protractor level

Activity 29
1a. $\dfrac{9}{r} = \dfrac{12}{r + 4}$ **1b.** 12 km/h, 16 km/h **2a.** $r + 10$

2b. width; $\dfrac{135}{r} = \dfrac{195}{r + 10}$; 22.5 mph, 32.5 mph

3a. $t - 1$ **3b.** $65(t - 1), 60t$
3c. $65(t - 1) = 60t, t = 13$ hours **3d.** 13 h, 12 h

Activity 30
3. 24 **7.** 2 **8.** 4 **9.** 1 **10.** 6 **11.** 6; yes

Activity 31
1. The models for both the expressions are the same.
2. The graphs for both the expressions are the same.
3. The two expressions are equivalent.

Activity 32
1. Answers may vary. Graphs should approach 50% as number of tosses increases. **2.** Answers may vary. The experimental probability of heads and tails becomes closer to the theoretical probability of 50%.

Activity 33
1. No. There is probably more than one y for some value of x.
2. Yes. There is exactly one y for each value of x.
3. No. There will be more than one y for some value of x.
4. Answers may vary. **5.** At any point, a vertical line will intersect the graph only once. **6.** At some points, a vertical line will intersect the graph more than once.
7–8. Answers may vary.

Activity 34
1–5. Answers may vary. **6.** Yes **7.** Answers may vary.
8. Yes **9.** Yes **10.** Answers may vary. **11.** Yes

Activity 35
1–2. Answers may vary. **3.** Yes; Yes **4.** Yes

Activity 36
1. Each DF provides a straight line along which the flash event occurred. The intersection of the two lines points to the exact location of the lightning. **2.** (11, 118) **3.** $y = 10.73x$
4. Go 11 miles east and turn north and go 118 miles.

Activity 37
1–6. Answers may vary.

Activity 38
1. Third **2.** Third **3.** Yes **4.** First row, first column
5–7. Answers may vary.

Activity 39
1. Same-size matrices can be added **2.** To multiply two matrices, the number of columns in first matrix should equal the number of rows in the second column. Orientation of a matrix makes a difference; 2×3 is different from 3×2.
3. $n \times m$ matrix multiplied by $m \times p$ matrix gives $n \times p$ matrix **4.** Not necessarily, multiplying two square matrices gives a square matrix of the same size. **5.** Yes

Activity 40
1. Sample parabola:

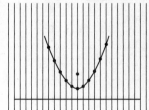

Activity 41
1–4. Answers may vary.

Activity 42
Student 1:
1. i **2.** 1 **3.** $-i$ **4.** $-i$ **5.** 1 **6.** i **7.** -1 **8.** $-i$ **9.** i **10.** $-i$
Student 2:
1. i **2.** $-i$ **3.** $-i$ **4.** $-i$ **5.** -1 **6.** $-i$ **7.** -1 **8.** i
9. $-i$ **10.** $-i$

Activity Answers (continued)

Activity 43

1–6. Check students' work, or let them check each other's work. Quotients are given. **1.** $x + 3$ **2.** $x - 2$ **3.** $x - 3$
4. $x - 5$ **5.** $x + 4 + \dfrac{-1}{x - 2}$ **6.** $x + 7 + \dfrac{5}{x - 2}$

Activity 44

1. 3 **2.** 1 hill, 1 valley **3.** 1 hill, 1 valley
4–10. Check students' graphs. **6.** 2 hills, 2 valleys
7. Exercise 2 **8.** Exercise 4 **9.** 2 hills, 1 valley or 1 hill, 2 valleys **10.** The ends both point in the same direction.

Activity 45

1a. 4 and 9 **1b.** $\sqrt{4}$ and $\sqrt{9}$ **2a.** Measure the length of one side of the square **2b.** 4 inches long **3.** 36 square inches
4. Cube **5a.** 16 **5b.** $\sqrt{16}$

Activity 46

Group activity in which students sharpen their mental math skills in solving simple radical equations.

Activity 47

1.

disks	1	2	3	4	5
moves	1	3	7	15	31

2. 2, 4, 8, 16 **3.** $2^1, 2^2, 2^3, 2^4$
4. $2^1 - 1, 2^2 - 1, 2^3 - 1, 2^4 - 1$
5. $m = 2^d - 1$
6.

d	6	7	8
m	63	127	255

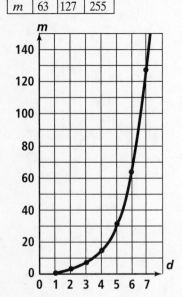

Activity 48

1. Yes **2.** No **3.** $I_{max} = 10^{10.5} I_0$
4. 112 decibel **5.** Yes **6.** $I_{max} = 10^{12} I_0$ **7.** No
8. Yes **9.** $I_{max} = 10^{14} I_0$

Activity 49

1. 7.5 **2.** 12 **3.** Check sudents' work **4.** 20, 3.2 **5.** 9.6, 5
6. 10, 4.5, 7.5, 18

Activity 50

1. Table 1 second column: $\frac{2}{3}, \frac{7}{8}, \frac{117}{118}$;
Table 2 second column: $\frac{2}{3}, \frac{7}{8}, \frac{117}{118}$;
The answers were the same. It took longer to evaluate the expression in Table 1 than in Table 2. **2.** Answers may vary.
3. $\dfrac{(x - 7)(x - 2)}{(x - 5)(x + 1)}$ **4.** Answers may vary.

Activity 51

1. Oval-shaped curve called an ellipse **2.** From P, measure PF_1 and PF_2. For any point P on the ellipse, $PF_1 + PF_2 = C$ for a constant C. **3.** As you bring the two points F_1 and F_2 closer, the ellipse becomes more circular. Moving the two points F_1 and F_2 apart makes the ellipse longer and narrower.
4. The ellipse becomes bigger for longer strings. **5.** Circle

Activity 52

1. Check students' work. **2.** When the plane is parallel to the cone's base, the intersection gives a circle. **3.** To generate an ellipse, the plane should be at an angle as it cuts through the cone. To get a parabola, the plane should be through the cone.
4. A point, the plane intersects the vertex of the cone.
5. A conic section is formed by the intersection of a plane and a cone. For a hyperbola, a plane intersects a double cone perpendicular to the bases of the cones.

Activity 53

1. 16 **2.** Students arrange the counters. **3.** 9 **4.** 4
5. 1, 4, 9, 16 **6.** Same as in Exercise 5 **7.** $S_n = n^2$
8. 25; 49; 10,000 **9.** −10 **10.** 21

Activity 54

1. Answers may vary.
2. $a_2 + a_5 = (a_1 + d) + (a_6 - d) = a_1 + a_6$
3. 3 **4.** Answers may vary. **5.** Answers may vary. **6.** a_4
7. Answers may vary. **8.** a_4 **9.** Answers may vary. **10.** S_7

Activity 55

1–2. Answers may vary. **3.** $\frac{3}{8}$ **4.** Answers may vary.

Activity 56

1. This data set should approximate a normal distribution.
2–4. Check students' work. **5.** Check students' work. Expect about 68% of the heights to fall within one standard deviation.
6. Check students' work. **7.** Check students' work. Expect about 95% of the heights to fall within two standard deviations. **8–9.** Check students' work.

Activity Answers (continued)

Activity 57

1.

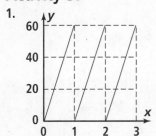

2. yes   **3.** 1 min.   **4.** Starts at 1 min. rather than at 0, ends at 4 min.   **5.** Starts at −2 min. rather than 0, ends at 1 min.

6.

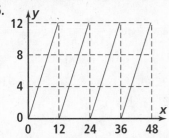

7. 12 h   **8.** Z

9.

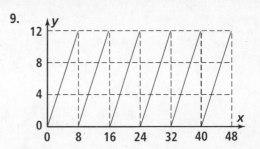

10. 8 h   **11.** would start at −16 h and run until 32 h
12. 6 h   **13.** 4

Activity 58

1. 20°   **2.** Yes   **3.** Yes   **4.** 83°   **5.** 57°   **6.** 46°   **7.** 67°   **8.** 61°
9. 27°   **10.** 35°   **11.** 58°

Activity 59

1. a **2.** b **3.** b **4.** a **5.** b **6.** $-a$ **7.** 0   **8.** $\alpha - \beta = 90°$
and $\cos(90°) = 0$ **9.** 1   **10.** $\alpha - \beta = 90°$ and $\sin(90°) = 1$